THE COMPLETE PIANO
NASHVILLE HIT

Arranged by Kenneth Baker

GW00836646

Wise Publications
London/New York/Sydney/Cologne

Exclusive distributors:
Music Sales Limited
8/9 Frith Street, London W1V 5TZ, England.
Music Sales Pty Limited
120 Rothschild Avenue, Rosebery, NSW 2018, Australia.

This book © Copyright 1988 by
Wise Publications
UK ISBN 0.7119.1531.8
Order No. AM71879

Designed by Pearce Marchbank Studio
Compiled by Peter Evans
Arranged by Kenneth Baker

Music Sales' complete catalogue lists thousands of
titles and is free from your local music shop,
or direct from Music Sales
Limited. Please send 50p in stamps for postage to
Music Sales Limited, 8/9 Frith Street, London W1V 5TZ.

Printed in the United Kingdom by
J.B. Offset Printers (Marks Tey) Limited, Marks Tey, Essex.

COLD, COLD HEART

Words & Music by Hank Williams

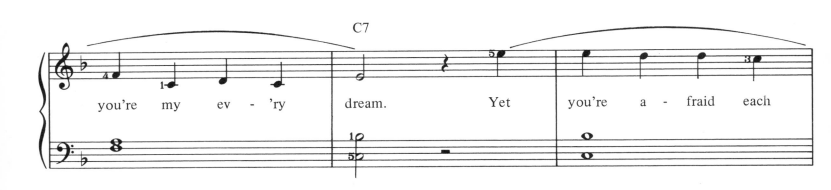

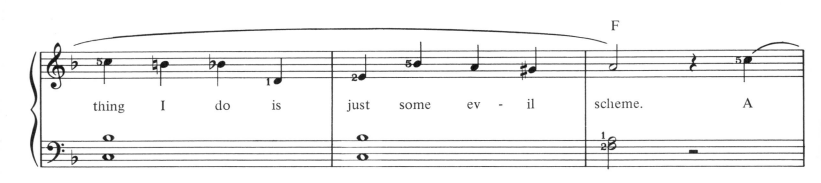

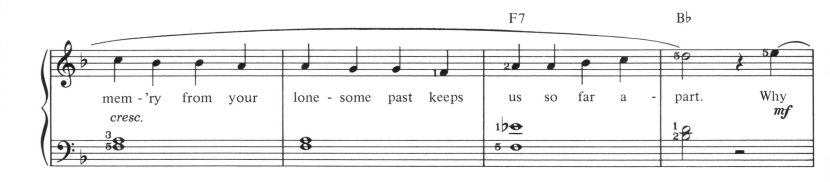

can't I free your doubt - ful mind, and melt your cold, cold heart? An -

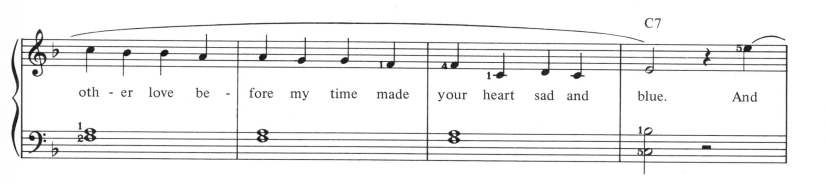

oth - er love be - fore my time made your heart sad and blue. And

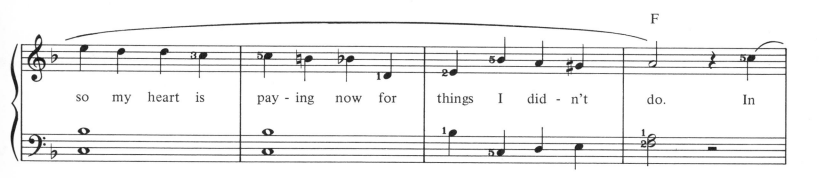

so my heart is pay - ing now for things I did - n't do. In

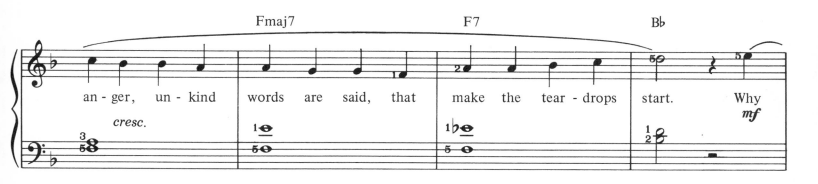

an - ger, un - kind words are said, that make the tear - drops start. Why

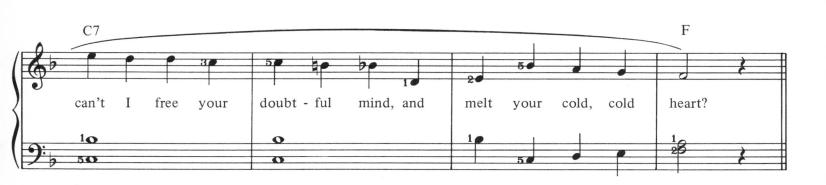

can't I free your doubt - ful mind, and melt your cold, cold heart?

DEVOTED TO YOU

Words & Music by Boudleaux Bryant

Simply ♩ = 96

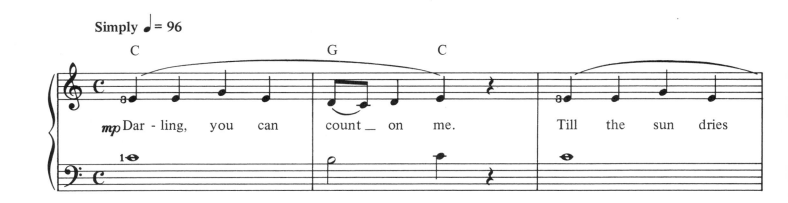

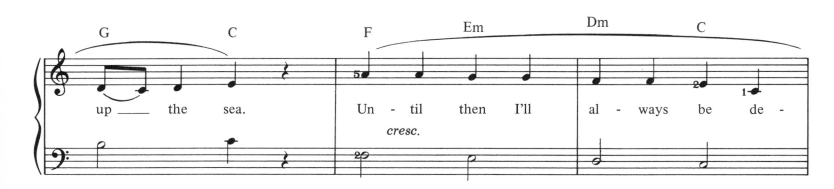

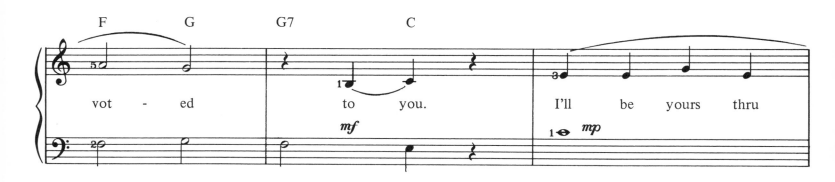

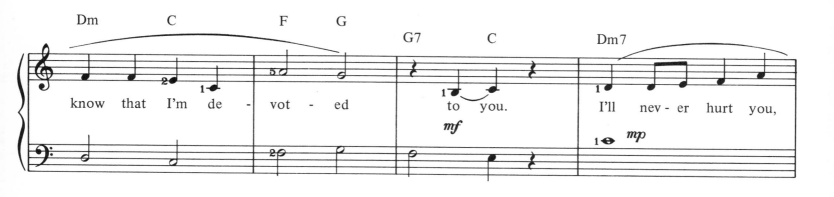

know that I'm de - vot - ed   to you.   I'll nev - er hurt you,

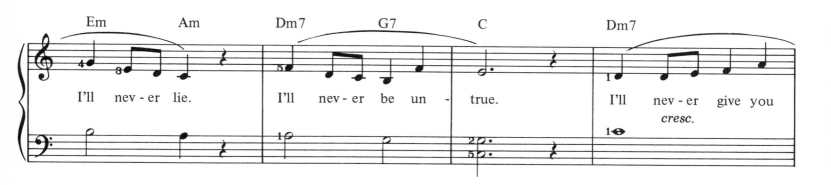

I'll nev - er lie.   I'll nev - er be un - true.   I'll nev - er give you

rea - son to cry.   I'd be un - hap - py if   you were blue. ___   Thru the years my

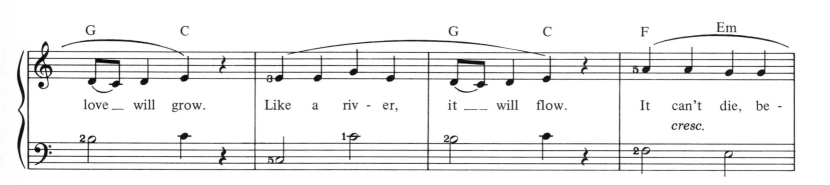

love ___ will grow.   Like a riv - er,   it ___ will flow.   It can't die, be -

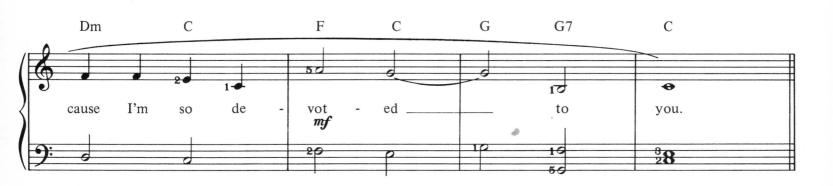

cause I'm so de - vot - ed _____   to   you.

BYE BYE LOVE

Words & Music by Felice & Boudleaux Bryant

Quite fast ♩ = 160

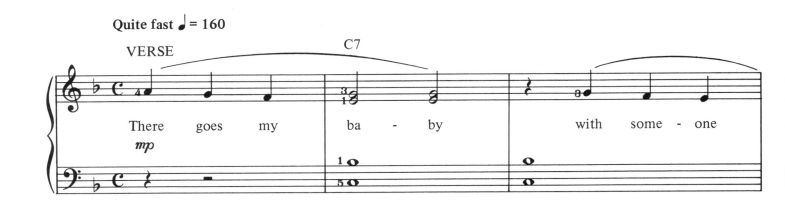

There goes my ba - by with some - one

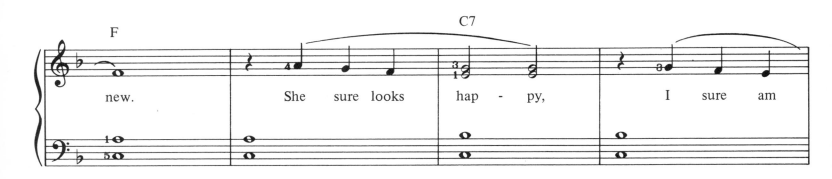

new. She sure looks hap - py, I sure am

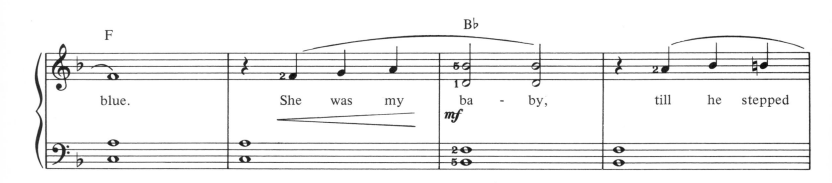

blue. She was my ba - by, till he stepped

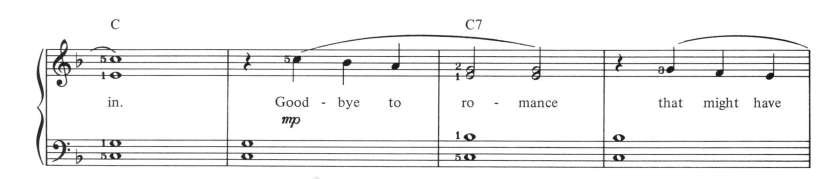

in. Good - bye to ro - mance that might have

CHORUS

9

RELEASE ME

Words & Music by Eddie Miller, Dub Williams, Robert Yount & Robert Harris

MAKE THE WORLD GO AWAY

Words & Music by Hank Cochran

I'M SO LONESOME I COULD CRY

Words & Music by Hank Williams

DISTANT DRUMS

Words & Music by Cindy Walker

TAKE A MESSAGE TO MARY

Words & Music by Felice & Boudleaux Bryant

FUNNY, FAMILIAR, FORGOTTEN FEELINGS

Words & Music by Mickey Newbury

CATHY'S CLOWN

Words & Music by Don & Phil Everly

YOUR CHEATIN' HEART

Words & Music by Hank Williams

heart will tell on you. When tears come

down like fall-in' rain. ___ You'll toss a-

round, and call my name. You'll walk ___ the

floor, the way I do, your cheat-in'
cresc.

heart will tell on you.

25

SHE WEARS MY RING

Words & Music by Felice & Boudleaux Bryant

JAMBALAYA (ON THE BAYOU)

Words & Music by Hank Williams

FUNNY HOW TIME SLIPS AWAY

Words & Music by Willie Nelson

I CAN'T STOP LOVING YOU

Words & Music by Don Gibson

PICK ME UP ON YOUR WAY DOWN

Words & Music by Harlan Howard

ROCKY TOP

Words & Music by Boudleaux & Felice Bryant

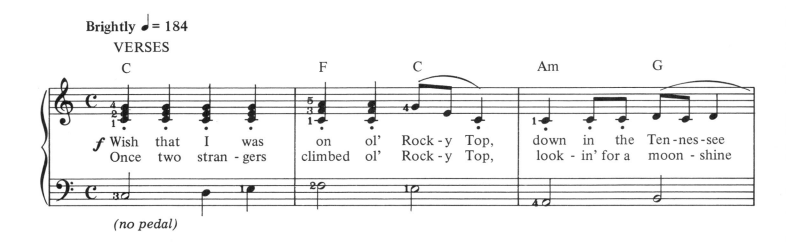

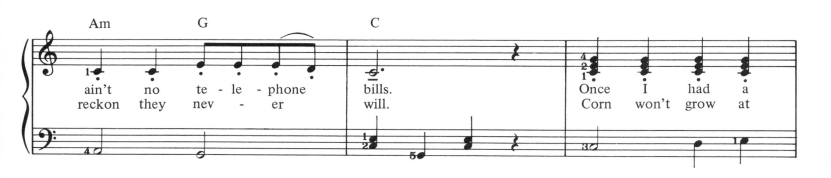

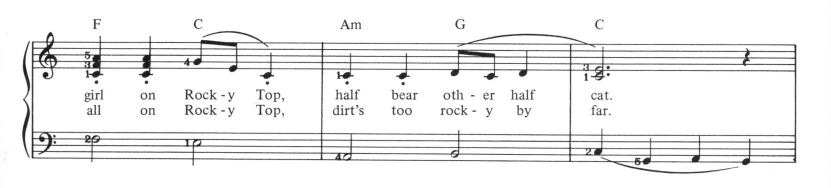

CHORUS

37

THERE GOES MY EVERYTHING

Words & Music by Dallas Frazier

CHORUS

39

ALL I HAVE TO DO IS DREAM

Words & Music by Boudleaux Bryant

HEY, GOOD LOOKIN'

Words & Music by Hank Williams

we could find us a brand new re - ci - pe? I got a

hot rod Ford, and a two dol-lar bill, and I know a spot right o -ver the hill.

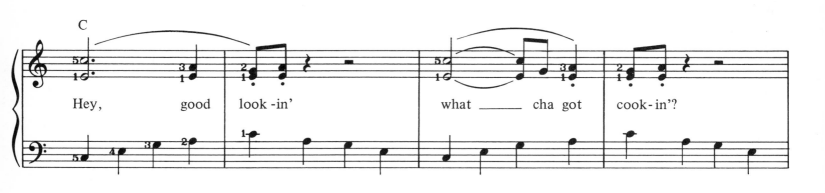

There's so-da pop and the danc - in's free, so if you wan-na have fun, come a - long with me.

Hey, good look -in' what _____ cha got cook-in'?

How's a - bout cook - in' some - thing up with me?

TAKE THESE CHAINS FROM MY HEART

Words & Music by Fred Rose & Hy Heath

BIRD DOG

Words & Music by Boudleaux Bryant

CHORUS